D1562320

GENETICS AND MODERN BIOLOGY

MEMOIRS OF THE
AMERICAN PHILOSOPHICAL SOCIETY
Held at Philadelphia
For Promoting Useful Knowledge

VOLUME 57

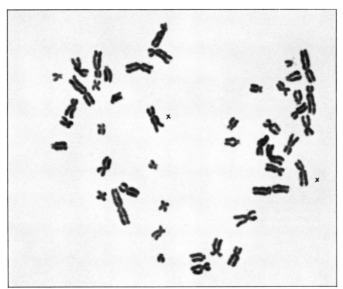

FIG. 1. Normal human female somatic chromosomes.
The two X chromosomes are indicated (by ca. 1300).
From J. H. Tjio and T. T. Puck, Proc. Nat. Acad. Sci.
44:(1958): 1229.

FIG. 2. Location of DNA in salivary gland
chromosomes of the fruit fly, revealed by
fluorescence microscopy. Photography by Berwind
H. Kaufmann, Genetics Research Unit,
Carnegie Institution of Washington.

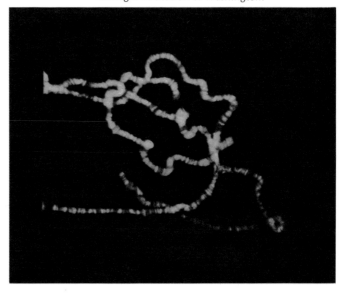

GENETICS
AND
MODERN BIOLOGY

GEORGE W. BEADLE

President, University of Chicago

Jayne Lectures for 1962

QH431
B36g
1963

AMERICAN PHILOSOPHICAL SOCIETY
INDEPENDENCE SQUARE
PHILADELPHIA
1963

161456

The Jayne Lectures of the American Philosophical Society honor the memory of Henry La Barre Jayne, 1857-1920, a distinguished citizen of Philadelphia and an honored member of the Society. They perpetuate in this respect the aims of the American Society for the Extension of University Teaching, in which Mr. Jayne was deeply interested. When in 1946 this organization was dissolved, having in large measure fulfilled its immediate purposes, its funds were transferred to the American Philosophical Society, which agreed to use them "for the promotion of university teaching, including *inter alia* lectures, publications and research in the fields of science, literature, and the arts."

Accepting this responsibility, the Society initiated in 1961 a series of lectures to be given annually or biennially by outstanding scholars, scientists, and artists, and to be published in book form by the Society. The lectures will be presented in successive years at the University of Pennsylvania, the Franklin Institute, the Free Library of Philadelphia, and the Philadelphia Museum of Art.

The second series, constituting the present volume, was delivered by Dr. George Wells Beadle, on March 7, 14 and 21, 1962 in the Museum of the University of Pennsylvania, under the joint auspices of that institution and the American Philosophical Society.

COPYRIGHT © 1963 BY THE AMERICAN PHILOSOPHICAL SOCIETY

*Library of Congress Catalog
Card Number: 63-21535*

PREFACE

For its second series of Jayne Lectures, presented in 1962, the American Philosophical Society chose a topic of timely importance and a speaker uniquely prepared to discuss it. The genetic mechanism—the process by which hereditary factors determine the bodily structure and even the detailed characteristics of the succeeding generation, has been one of the greatest mysteries of science. To its investigation George Wells Beadle, sometime professor at Stanford University, and later at the California Institute of Technology at Pasedena, has devoted his entire career. In recent years, as the problem came more and more to depend upon chemistry for its ultimate solution, Dr. Beadle has been one of the foremost students of biochemical genetics. His investigation, with Edward L. Tatum, of the way in which hereditary factors operate in the nutritional chemistry of a certain lowly organism—*Neurospora,* little known outside biological laboratories, but specially suitable for genetic research —won for the two of them in 1958 the Nobel Prize for medicine and physiology. No one could be found better qualified than Dr. Beadle by experience in both the biological and chemical aspects of genetics, and by skill in scientific exposition, to deal with this fascinating but complex subject.

The problem which the biochemists had to answer was: how can the arrangement of atoms and groups of atoms within a chromosome control the exact organization of bodily details, directing a given tissue to acquire a certain color, a given extremity to arrange itself in a special form, or a given organ to take on a specific physiological function? Within the past two decades we have begun to learn the answer to this most fundamental question of biological science. The chromosomes are made up largely of nucleoproteins, complex substances whose very large molecules consist of hundreds of chemical sub-units arranged in regular sequences. Such sequences constitute the "genetic code" by which the chemical factors of heredity direct the production and organization of the diverse materials of the developing body of a plant or animal.

The code has now been partially deciphered. Its general arrangement begins to be understood, and some of its signals can be conjecturally identified. Before us lies a vast field of research with infinite possibilities for the increase of human knowledge and the control of inheritance. This is the subject which Dr. Beadle undertook to discuss for the educated public in his Jayne Lectures for 1962.

After he accepted the lectureship, Dr. Beadle was elected President of the University of Chicago. In spite of all the extra work and distractions connected with moving from California to Illinois and assuming a new post with heavy responsibilities, he faithfully kept his appointment with the American Philosophical Society. Speaking in an informal and exceptionally clear style, Dr. Beadle three times filled the large auditorium of the University of Pennsylvania Museum with an enthusiastic audience of university people of all ranks and degrees of scientific experience, and won the highest appreciation of laymen as well as biologists and biochemists for the brilliant and instructive discourses here presented in print.

CONTENTS

GENETICS AND MODERN BIOLOGY

I. MENDEL TO WATSON AND CRICK

EACH OF US starts development as a single, almost microscopic cell, the fertilized egg. This cell is about one three-hundredth of an inch in diameter. Well lighted on a proper background, it would be just barely visible to the naked eye. This tiny cell must contain directions or specifications for making a person, given a suitable environment and a proper supply of raw material. It seldom makes a mistake. It does not look very different from the egg of a rabbit, a guinea pig, or an elephant. In fact, it does not even look so very different from the cell that gives rise to a spinach plant. But obviously these several kinds of cells "know" what they are going to become. They never make a mistake so gross as to give rise to the wrong kind of an animal. Furthermore, the human egg does not just give rise to just any person; it develops into a very specific person such as one of us. As you know, each of us is unique, different in some degree from every other person on earth.

The geneticist asks a series of questions about these specifications—this coded information that says how to make a person out of a cell that superficially looks so simple.

First, the geneticist wants to know how we receive these instructions from our parents and how we transmit them to our children. This is the substance of classical genetics.

Second, we want to know how these specifications are written. What is the language of genetics?

Third, how are the directions copied? With each cell division in the germ line, the total specification must be copied with a high degree of precision. In fact, we believe that they are copied with similar accuracy with each of many millions of cell divisions in all parts of the body. The question of how they are copied is a question of primary importance to all of biology.

Fourth, we want to know how this special language is translated. How do we use the directions in such a tiny cell to make one of us?

Finally, we want to know how it is that the specifications occasionally become modified, for this is the basis of our individual uniqueness. Such modifications are a basic part of the process of organic evolution.

At this point I propose to review some special aspects of the history of genetics that are of special interest to me and that may not be generally known.

Gregor Mendel

Going back a century to Gregor Mendel who, as you know, discovered the basic laws of inheritance, I remind you that he worked on the common garden pea and found that the material of inheritance in that plant is transmitted as a series of discrete units. He called them elements. We call them genes. He discovered that homologous units (alleles) from different varieties show dominance and recessiveness. For example, round seeds are dominant to wrinkled seeds. He showed that the units associated with separate characters are segregated quite independently of one another in passing from one generation to the next. He also pointed out that unlike alleles, for example those for round and wrinkled seeds, emerge from a hybrid quite uncontaminated. That is, if two allelic genes from parents that differ in seed shape go into an individual, they come out in its offspring as they went in.

It is an interesting fact that every one of these laws of Mendel has had to be modified in significant ways. In detail he was wrong on every count. But as a first approximation he was right. This, of course, is often the case in science. Newton's laws of motion are approximately correct but were shown by Einstein and others to require modification in ways that are of great significance under special conditions.

There are other interesting aspects of Mendel's work. In his time chromosomes, in which genes are carried, had not yet been discovered. His units of inheritance were hypothetical as far as their material substance was concerned. In a sense he predicated that chromosomes ought to exist. They were identified as the probable carriers of genes some thirty-five years after Mendel published his findings on inheritance in the garden pea.

The seven different characters with which Mendel worked were all inherited independently. We know now that the genes concerned are located in the seven different chromosomes of the pea plant. We know too that there are only seven different paired chromosomes in this plant. Mendel was incredibly fortunate, for the chance that seven different gene pairs picked at random would be carried in seven different chromosome pairs, assuming chromosomes of equal genetic size, is $1 \times 6/7 \times 5/7 \times 4/7 \times 3/7 \times 2/7 \times 1/7 = 1/163.4$. This says that his *a priori* chance of picking seven gene pairs located in seven different chromosomes was only about one in 163. Actually the odds against him were not that great, for had some of the genes he worked with been linked but so loosely as to appear to segregate independently, he would have found agreement of his hypothesis with the observed results. Nevertheless, had he not been so remarkably fortunate, he could easily have been confused by the phenomenon we now call linkage and not have formulated the laws of inheritance that now carry his name.

Another remarkable aspect of Mendel's results is the closeness with which the ratios he reported agree with the so-called expected or ideal ratios. Some years ago the statistician R. A. Fisher calculated that, if one were to repeat Mendel's total series of experiments in the same manner and were dealing with random sampling of infinite populations in which ratios were perfect, one would have a negligibly small chance of getting as close a fit as Mendel reported. The implication is clear that Mendel was not completely objective about his experiments. But I hasten to point out that this need not have been in any dishonest way. How then could he have come so close? It is almost certain that he knew what he expected before all the experiments were completed. In other words, he formulated his hypothesis part way along and then did further experiments to test it. No doubt Mendel was emotionally biased in favor of the hypothesis. He hoped it would be correct. Since he did not well understand statistics and theory of sampling, he probably did what many of us would do today. Presumably he scored a reasonable number of segregating families, say for round and wrinkled seeds. Say he expected a 3:1 ratio. If the sums were a close fit, he would be tempted not to score more. If the "fit" were not as good as he hoped, he would be tempted to score more, stopping when the results satisfied him. This we now know is not completely objective experimentation. But it is not an unusual practice. Most persons who have carried out laboratory experiments have succumbed to the temptation to stop when the results "seemed" right. If in plotting measurements that fall on a smooth curve one suddenly finds a measurement that does not fit well, the natural assumption is that there must have been a mistake. If on repeating the measurement the fit is good, it is assumed that this is correct and the previous measurement erroneous. However, unless there is independent evidence of such an error, this is not, strictly speaking, an objective and fair way of carrying out an experiment. On the other hand, some intuitive feeling of when the results are right is important in science, for otherwise one would spend an inordinate amount of time finding out the precise ways in which errors are made. I believe Mendel had a well-developed intuitive sense of this kind. Like many other good scientists, he was not an impassionate, insensitive, wholly objective person, interested solely in discovering the truth. Instead, like most of us in similar circumstances, he almost certainly hoped to find that his hypothesis was correct.

Morgan and Emerson

By the end of the first decade of the present century, Thomas Hunt Morgan had acquired an international reputation as an embryologist. Like many of his contemporaries in the classical branches of biology of that time, he looked with a good deal of skepticism on the newly rediscovered Mendelian laws. In 1908 he delivered a paper before the American Breeders' Association (*Report* 5: 365-368, 1908) in which he expressed his doubts in no uncertain terms. Attending the same meeting was the American geneticist Rollins Adams Emerson, already converted to the new discipline, scheduled to give a paper on coat color inheritance in beans, immediately following Morgan.

In a friendly spirit Morgan chided the geneticists, pointing out that their game of juggling hypothetical units of inheritance was much too easy and therefore not convincing. Among other things, he said,

In the modern interpretation of Mendelism, facts are being transformed into factors at a rapid rate. If one factor will not explain the facts, then two are invoked; if two prove insufficient, three will sometimes work out. The superior jugglery sometimes necessary to account for the results may sometimes blind us, if taken too naively, to the commonplace that the results are often so excellently "explained" because the explanation was invented to explain them. We work backward from the facts to the factors, and then, presto explain the facts by the very factors that we invented to explain them.

In Emerson's paper, immediately following Morgan's (*Report* 5: 368-376, 1908), a case of inheritance of coat color mottling in beans was reported in which a previously postulated one-gene hypothesis did not agree with the observed results. But, said Emerson, by assuming two segregating pairs of factors, results were readily accounted for.

Emerson's paper brought down the house; It seemed, just as Morgan had said, a great game. But what did it mean? Morgan had apparently won the day. The fact is Emerson was right, as subsequent tests of his hypothesis clearly showed.

A year or two later Morgan began his studies on *Drosophila*. In one of his cultures a white-eyed male appeared—the first recorded genetic mutation in this species. Morgan soon demonstrated that the white-eye character was inherited as a simple sex-linked character. Morgan had become a geneticist.

A short time later a second sex-linked character, miniature wing, was found. What would be the offspring of a female fly with the white-eye mutant gene in one X-chromosome and the miniature-wing gene in its homolog? The experiment was made. As every student of beginning genetics now knows, the male offspring included not only the two parental types, one with white eyes and normal wings and one with red eyes and miniature wings, but two new types, one red-eyed with normal wings and a double mutant type with white eyes and miniature wings. This now classical experiment and confirming ones with other sex-linked characters were interpreted in terms of physical exchange of corresponding segments of the two X-chromosome homologs in doubly heterozygous females. This exchange was called crossing over. The phenomenon and its explanation were duly reported in the scientific literature.

No sooner had Emerson learned of this new hypothesis of linkage with crossing over than he began to wonder how it could be reconciled with Mendel's basic law of the purity of the gametes. If genes were in chromosomes, and chromosomes underwent crossing over during the reduction divisions, wouldn't the crossover points sometimes fall within paired alleles? And if this were to happen wouldn't it follow that alleles would not come out of a hybrid as they went in? In a paper in *Science* in 1911 (34: 512-513), Emerson pointed out this objection to the Morgan hypothesis of crossing over, saying, " . . . *it certainly will not account for the purity of extracted recessives and dominants as exhibited by their behavior in F_3 and later generations. To overlook this is to neglect the fundamental part of Mendelism.*" (Italics are Emerson's.) This time it appeared that Emerson had won the verbal argument. But, no, it appeared that Morgan was right. Physical crossing over between homologous chromosomes not only does occur but it is in fact a normal part of the process of meiosis by which chromosomes are reduced to the single sets in the gametes or their precursor cells.

We can now write another paragraph to this chapter of genetics. It turns out, after all, that crossovers do occur within genes. Thus alleles do cross-contaminate. Mendel, Morgan, Emerson, and others failed to discover this for the simple reason that the gene pairs with which they worked differed in only one internal mutational site. Two such differences within a single gene pair are necessary to demonstrate intragenic crossing over (cross contamination of alleles), as we shall point out later.

In certain respects, both Morgan and Emerson were right in these two friendly arguments. And, having had the privilege of working in the laboratories of both men, I can assure you that they were both warm, sensitive human beings as well as great scientists. I am sure Mendel must have been the same.

Biochemical Genetics

I now turn to a subdivision of genetics we call biochemical genetics. Classical genetics deals with the manner in which organisms receive genes from their parents and how they transmit them to their offspring. In the early stages classical genetics had little to say about what genes are. They were purely hypothetical units. Of course early workers wondered what they were, physically and chemically. And, although it took a long time to find this out, very early after the rediscovery of Mendel in 1900, thirty-five years after the publication of his paper, the English physician and biochemist, Sir Archibald Garrod, became interested in some human diseases that suggested an answer. He called these particular diseases inborn errors of metabolism. One of them, called albinism, involves lack of melanin pigment. The white, pink-eyed rabbit is an albino. A homologous character appears in man. It is also known in a number of other animals.

Garrod investigated another inborn error called alcaptonuria. This is a disease in which the affected individual is unable to metabolize alcapton, which chemically is known as 2,5-dihydroxyphenyl-acetic acid. Alcaptonurics cannot break the benzene ring of this molecule. As a result, they excrete alcapton in the urine. Alcapton has the property of turning black on exposure to air. Alcaptonuria is therefore sometimes called the black urine disease. It is a very rare disease, and fortunately not a serious one. It is expressed at birth and persists throughout life. Garrod knew the biochemical nature of this disease. He also discovered, after talking with the geneticist Bateson and checking appropriate pedigrees, that it is inherited as a simple Mendelian recessive. He concluded quite correctly that the normal allele of the gene concerned somehow says that particular chemical reaction will occur. Since Garrod also knew of the existence of enzymes as organic catalysts, he further concluded that the mutant gene must be modified in such a way that an enzyme responsible for the cleavage of the alcapton benzene ring is absent or inactive. Thus he is responsible for the concept that this gene controls a chemical reaction through an enzyme as an intermediary. This was an important landmark in biochemical genetics.

Garrod's investigations on this and other genetic diseases were summarized in a now classical book, *Inborn Errors of Metabolism,* published in 1909. A second edition appeared in 1923. A few geneticists referred to it in the early days, Bateson among them, but there was a long period of about thirty years during which geneticists failed to refer to this clear case of interrelation between a gene, an enzyme, and a chemical reaction. Like Mendel, Garrod was ahead of his time by a third of a century. In partial explanation, let me remind you that in 1923 nobody knew the chemical nature of enzymes. Even after the enzyme urease was isolated in crystalline form in 1926 by Sumner at Cornell University and shown to be a protein, biochemists remained skeptical. Only a decade later was it finally agreed that all enzymes either are or contain proteins and that they act as specific catalysts by virtue of their protein components.

Following Garrod, other people worked on various organisms from the point of view of what genes do. One category of reactions that were worked on was that having to do with flower pigments. A group of English investigators, including Onslow, Haldane, Scott-Moncrieff, and others, have investigated flower pigments and their genetic control. The red and blue anthocyanins and related yellow and orange are the pigments that give flowers their color. Here again, it can be demonstrated that there is a relation between gene and specific reaction as postulated by Garrod.

I should add that Garrod used alcaptonuric subjects in a very interesting way. He postulated that alcapton came from the amino acid phenylalanine which we get in our food. Some phenylalanine molecules are oxidized to tyrosine and then through a series of reactions to alcapton and finally to carbon dioxide and water. When the breakdown of alcapton is blocked, it is excreted by the kidney. If alcaptonurics are fed precursors of alcapton, such as phenylalanine or tyrosine, the excretion of alcapton is increased. In this way Garrod identified a number of precursors of alcapton. This valuable biochemical tool is much used today in identifying metabolic pathways. Garrod developed it. Modern biochemists have rediscovered it.

Eye Colors in Drosophila

I now turn to a separate line of investigation that led to conclusions very much like those of Garrod. Back in 1933, a Russian scientist, Boris Ephrussi, who much earlier had moved to Paris, came to the California Institute of Technology as a Rockefeller Foundation Fellow. He was interested in embryology and genetics. He and I often talked about a question that many embryologists and geneticists had long worried about: Why doesn't someone find a way to relate genetics and embryology? Part of the reason no one had done so, we said, was that the organisms traditionally used in embryology were not good for genetic studies— sea urchins, for example. On the other hand, the organisms used in genetics were not favorable for embryological studies—*Drosophila,* for example. Thinking that we ought to do something about this situation, we both took a year off and ventured the attempt. Deciding that the best organism to begin with would be *Drosophila,* we optimistically set out to find out something about its embryology and larval development. I went to Paris and worked at Ephrussi's laboratory. At that time he was using tissue-culture techniques, so I started by learning about tissue culture. In those days tissue culture was difficult, involving work under strictly aseptic conditions. We tried to culture *Drosophila* tissues but had no success. Ephrussi suggested we try transplantation. We were willing to try anything, so first we went to Professor Perez of the Sorbonne, a noted authority on insect development. He told us immediately that we could not have picked a worse organism. Flies, he said, were just impossible. In the larval stage there are many embryonic buds destined to become parts of the adult and they all look alike. He suggested that we go back to our laboratory and forget about it. Instead we went back and started dissecting *Drosophila* larvae. It looked pretty discouraging. We weren't able to identify much of anything. But we kept on trying by picking up embryonic buds in special micropipettes and transplanting them to the body cavities of host larvae. One morning we came to the laboratory and found a fly that had three eyes. So we knew we had transplanted an eye bud. Then we wondered whether we could do it again.

We went to our favorite cafe and sat there all day drinking coffee and discussing what we would do next. We had a technique, but what to do with it? We recalled that Professor Sturtevant had found that vermilion eye in *Drosophila* behaved in genetic mosaics in a non-autonomous manner. Vermilion flies have bright red eyes as compared with the dull red eye of wild-type flies. They differ from wild type in a sex-linked gene. If a female fly has a normal allele of vermilion in one sex chromosome and a vermilion allele in the homologous one, the chromosome carrying the normal allele is sometimes lost in half the body. In such a case the half with a single X-chromosome is male. The other half is female, as it should be. Such a fly is called a gynandromorph. Since the normal allele of the gene is lost, the male side should have a bright red eye. It should be vermilion in appearance. But Sturtevant found that sometimes it was not vermilion. Analyzing the situation by following other sex-linked characters such as yellow body color or forked bristles, he correctly assumed that some influence from non-vermilion parts of the body moves to the eye and causes it to be wild type, that is, not vermilion. We decided to investigate this. We transplanted vermilion eyes to wild-type larvae that would metamorphose into flies with normal dull red eyes. As expected, the implanted eyes were not vermilion. They had the wild-type dull red color. The obvious next problem was to identify this substance, something that moved from one part of the fly to another. The fact is we ended up finding two substances that worked in tandem. The first was converted into the second and that in turn was converted into pigment. We identified two genes, vermilion and cinnabar, that blocked two successive reactions. We could use one mutant type, cinnabar, to accumulate the first substance in much the same way as Garrod used alcaptonurics to accumulate and excrete alcapton. Ours was an example of a sequence of two successive reactions controlled by genes. We investigated all the eye-color mutants known in *Drosophila* and found that no other eye-color gene of the twenty-six then available had anything to do with these two reactions. On this basis we were led to postulate that each gene does but one task and in a primary sense does no more. This was the beginning, in our minds, of the so-called "one gene, one enzyme" hypothesis, later to become the "one gene, one protein" hypothesis. There followed a long period of trying to work out the chemistry of these substances, in Ephrussi's laboratory and at Stanford where Edward L. Tatum and I worked. We grew millions of wild-type or cinnabar flies and extracted the substances from them in the pupal stage. We came pretty close to determining what they were chemically but we did not succeed. Finally they were identified by Butenandt in Germany and Amano in Japan.

Neurospora

Before this was accomplished, Tatum and I hit upon the idea of reversing the procedure we had been using to identify specific genes with particular chemical reactions. We reasoned that, if the one primary function of a gene is to control a particular chemical reaction, why not begin with known chemical reactions and then look for the genes that control them? In this way we could stick to our specialty, genetics, and build on the work chemists had already done. The obvious approach was first to find an organism whose chemical reactions were well known and then induce mutations in it that would block specific identifiable reactions.   Bacteria were one possibility; many of them are known to synthesize their amino acids and vitamins from relatively simple starting materials such as sugar and inorganic salts.   The trouble with bacteria was that techniques for investigating them genetically were not yet developed.   Today they are well known and these organisms, especially the colon bacilli, are widely used in studies of chemical genetics.   Finally, we hit upon the idea of using the bread mold *Neurospora*.   We knew that it had many advantages from a genetic standpoint.   For Bernard O. Dodge and Carl C. Lindegren had already done extensive work on it from this point of view.

Back in 1928, Dodge and Shear, then at the Department of Agriculture (later Dodge moved to the New York Botanical Garden with a joint appointment at Columbia University), worked out the life cycle of this organism.   The perfect stage had not previously been discovered.   *Neurospora* is an ascomycete, which means a "sac fungus."   Its fruiting body contains many long sacs, each containing eight spores lined up in a single row.   These eight spores are the products of the reduction divisions.   After fertilization occurs the resulting diploid nucleus, which is located in the cell that is to become the ascus, immediately undergoes the two reduction divisions.   The spindles of the second of these lie in tandem in the developing spore sac.   A third division occurs, mitotic in nature, duplicating each of the four products of the reduction division.   These are lined up in a row.   Each of these is included in a black football-shaped ascus spore, which becomes binucleate through a second mitotic division.   It is a relatively simple matter to remove the eight mature spores from a single spore sac in the order in which they are originally arranged.   In this way the four products of a single set of reduction divisions can be studied genetically, each in duplicate.   Furthermore, it is clear just how these were produced spacially by the two reduction divisions.

Dodge was the first to do such studies on *Neurospora sitophila* and *crassa,* the latter of which we used. He soon found that these are heterothallic fungi. Four spores give rise to one sex, four to the other. The first mutant Dodge studied was called albino. It lacked yellow asexual spores. When crossed with a normal yellow strain, the eight spores from a single spore sac gave rise to four yellow and four albino progeny. This is, of course, the primary Mendelian ratio for a single gene pair. In most cases the four yellows came from one half of the spore sac, the four albinos from the other half. But occasionally he found yellows and albinos in alternating pairs. He was puzzled by that, for many of the textbooks at that time said the first reduction division reduced the chromosome number to a single set. In that case segregation of a heterozygous gene pair should always occur at the first reduction division to give four yellows at one end of the spore sac and four whites at the other end. Obviously the alternating pairs of whites and yellows were not consistent with this view.

Soon after this, Dodge gave a seminar in genetics at Cornell in which he presented these results. In his audience were several graduate students, I among them. We had just been learning about four-strand crossing-over in *Drosophila* and suggested that this would explain the results. Such crossing over between the centromere and the segregating gene pair would lead to segregation in the second reduction division instead of in the first. It turned out that this was the correct interpretation.

Dodge was one of the most enthusiastic scientists I ever knew and his enthusiasm was highly contagious. He kept Morgan, then at Columbia, fully informed about his work. He insisted that *Neurospora* was a more favorable organism for genetics than was *Drosophila*. Morgan listened quietly and sympathetically but did not abandon *Drosophila*. Dodge kept coming back, insisting that Morgan ought at least to try *Neurospora*. About that time Morgan moved to the California Institute of Technology. To placate Dodge he carried along a set of *Neurospora* cultures that Dodge had pressed on him. He transferred them a few times but never seriously investigated them. One day there came to Morgan's laboratory a young man, Carl C. Lindegren, who had worked as a bacteriologist, and wanted a degree in genetics. Morgan suggested he take over the cultures of *Neurospora* and see what he could make of them.

On the basis of what Dodge had discovered, Lindegren went ahead and worked out the genetics of *Neurospora* in a very elegant way. Soon after, I went to Caltech as a postdoctoral fellow, and thus learned about *Neurospora*. It was natural, therefore, that when Tatum and I were searching for the ideal organism for our new approach to chemical genetics, we should think of *Neurospora*. The only difficulty in using it was that we did not know its basic nutritional requirements. We suspected from work on related fungi that these would be simple. This turned out to be the case, for we soon discovered that *Neurospora crassa* will grow on a synthetic medium containing inorganic salts, a source of carbon and energy (sucrose, for example), and the one vitamin biotin. Fortunately biotin had just been discovered and made available, for otherwise we could not have carried out our planned attack.

What we did was first to induce mutations at random with ultraviolet or x-rays. Then we picked out individual spores after a sexual generation and grew them on a medium containing all the vitamins and all the amino acids we knew about. On this, a mutant strain unable to synthesize any component of this "complete" medium would be able to grow by virtue of the supplement. All single-spore cultures were then transferred, by asexual spores, to an unsupplemented medium containing the bare essential ingredients for growth of the wild-type mold. A mutant strain unable to synthesize all needed vitamins or amino acids would be unable to grow on such a minimal medium even though normally it would grow on the supplemented medium.

We knew the mutations we wanted had to occur—we had that much faith in our hypothesis that genes control chemical reactions by way of enzymes as intermediaries. But we had no way of knowing what the mutation frequency of such genes would be and we were afraid it would be so low that we would get discouraged and stop before we found a single one. Before we made any tests on minimal medium, we isolated 1,000 individual spores. This seemed like a large number at the time. We were not disappointed. In subsequent tests on minimal medium and on media with known supplements, the 299th spore isolated gave a strain that could not synthesize vitamin B-6. In the next 1,000, the 85th spore carried a mutant gene that prevented synthesis of vitamin B-1. To say we were happy would be a gross understatement. We were tremendously excited. We vowed to continue until we had ten such mutants. In fact we did much better. We soon had hundreds of them, and were soon convinced that for any chemical reaction for which an essential product could be identified and supplied through the culture medium we could find a mutation.

Having such mutants it was a simple matter to cross them with the original wild type and through the arrangement of normals and mutants among the eight spores of a spore sac to determine whether or not a single mutant gene was involved. If there are four mutant and four normal spores, it is a simple gene mutation; otherwise, it is not. It is as simple as that. No statistical problems are involved, because there must be four normals and four mutants in each sac, for all the products of meiosis are recovered. It turned out on making such tests that almost all our mutant strains were the result of single gene mutations. Our confidence was justified.

What had we done? In fact we had just rediscovered what Garrod had found thirty-eight years before, but we did not know that because we had not done our library work and did not know of Garrod's work. As a matter of fact, most of our predecessors who had written the standard books on genetics had also overlooked Garrod, or forgotten about him, despite the fact that the two editions of his book, *Inborn Errors of Metabolism,* are not in any sense rare or difficult to find.

Our work differed from Garrod's in two respects: First, geneticists and biochemists were prepared to accept our hypothesis in 1941 as they were not three or four decades earlier. Furthermore, we had demonstrated many examples of gene-controlled reactions involving vitamins and amino acids. Biochemists know that these are of basic importance to all organisms. Thus, in a long, roundabout way via alcaptonuria, flower pigments, eye-colors in insects, and bread mold, it became obvious that biochemists and geneticists have much in common.

Transformation

Back in 1928 another line of investigation was begun by the English bacteriologist, Griffith, that was to have far-reaching consequences. This involves the bacteria that cause pneumonia in man—the so-called pneumococci. These bacteria can be grown on artificial media in laboratory cultures. They are also capable of growing in mice. Both characteristics contribute to their usefulness for biochemical and genetic studies.

The pneumococci come in dozens of serological types, the type specificity residing in a gelatinous capsule consisting largely of polysaccharide. In laboratory cultures mutants are occasionally found that lack capsules and are incapable of producing disease. They are avirulent and have no type specificity. Such avirulent capsuleless strains produce characteristic "rough" colonies on culture plates, whereas their virulent counterparts produce glistening colonies called "smooth." Thus the mutants are easily identified.

Griffith discovered that if he inoculated mice simultaneously with a rough mutant, originally of type II, and heat-killed smooth pneumococci of type III, some of the mice became infected and died. Mice separately inoculated with either single strain were unaffected. From the infected mice that died he recovered live virulent bacteria of type III. It appeared that something from the heat-killed smooth-type III cells had restored virulence to the rough type II cells and had transformed them to type III. It was later shown that such "transformation" can be carried out in test-tube cultures under certain conditions.

Sixteen years later Avery, MacLeod, and McCarty, working at the Rockefeller Institute for Medical Research in New York, succeeded in identifying the specific transforming substance contributed by the heat-killed partner in the collaborating system. It was deoxyribonucleic acid, abbreviated DNA. DNA as pure as the methods available at that time could make it was effective as the specific type III agent in the transformation.

This suggested the possibility that actual genetic material was being transferred from the heat-killed type III smooth to the avirulent rough that had come originally by mutation from a type II smooth. This possibility that the gene might consist solely of DNA, or at least depend for its specificity on a DNA component was revolutionary indeed. Many geneticists attempted to find alternative explanations. One possibility was that the DNA was not absolutely pure and that the specific agent might be a contaminant, possibly protein. We know now, of course, that the simple explanation is correct. Whole genes or parts of them are actually transferred from donor to recipient in the process of transformation. And the effective agent is DNA, not protein.

Bacterial Genetics

Soon after the *Neurospora* work got well under way at Stanford, Tatum undertook to see whether "biochemical" mutants comparable to those of *Neurospora* could be found in the common colon bacillus, *Escherichia coli*. He soon found that the answer is yes. With these mutants it became possible to reinvestigate the long-standing question of whether bacteria might not undergo some type of sexual reproduction. There had been previous attempts by both cytologists and geneticists to answer this question with either negative or inconclusive results.

The problem was tackled with vigor by Joshua Lederberg and Tatum at Yale University, where Lederberg had come to work as a graduate student. Using genetically defective parental strains under cultural conditions that would permit only recombinants, symbiotic associations, or back mutations to multiply, it was soon demonstrated that some type of sexual union, followed by the production of genetic recombinants, does indeed occur. The details of the process are remarkable beyond anything that could have been imagined in advance of their discovery.

Colon bacilli come in two mating types or sexes. In the sexual phase of the life cycle, cells of opposite mating type pair and form a conjugation tube. One of the pair, the male if you like, contributes genetic material in the form of one chromosome to the recipient cell or female. The single chromosome of the donor cell moves through the conjugation tube rather slowly, beginning always at one predetermined end. After the migration of the male chromosome is completed, recombination between the donor and recipient chromosomes occurs. It is possible through such recombination to construct genetic maps of the bacterial chromosome by methods that are in principle like those used in higher organisms.

In this remarkable process the entire chromosome of the donor cell seldom moves into the recipient. A terminal segment of varying length usually fails to make the journey. It follows, therefore, that genes near the "head" of the chromosome are more likely to be transferred than are those nearer the "tail." This means that genetic recombination in the recipient cell occurs between one whole chromosome and a fragment of the homologous chromosome from the male.

The process by which chromosome transfer through the conjugation tube occurs can be interrupted artificially. One simple way to do this is to subject the conjugated pairs to shearing forces in a Waring blender, thus breaking the tube and the migrating chromosomes. The entire process of transfer takes about an hour to complete. By interrupting the process at various times after contact is made by mating partners, it is possible to map genes rather precisely from the head to the tail of the donor chromosome in terms of the time required for them to pass through the conjugation tube into the recipient cell. Thus in the first few minutes no genes other than those near the head of the donor chromosome are transferred. Maps made in this way agree perfectly with those made in the more conventional way through frequencies of recombination.

I have not told you all the story. The individual bacterial cells usually have more than one nucleus, sometimes a large number. Apparently only one of these participates in the sexual transfer as far as the donor cell is concerned. The chromosome map is circular, suggesting that the one chromosome per nucleus is also circular. If so, in the transfer process it must open up. Just where this opening occurs is predetermined in particular strains. Thus the position of the "head" of the chromosome differs in different strains.

Sexual difference is dependent on a so-called "F" factor that is cytoplasmic under some circumstances. But it can also become attached to the circular chromosome at any one of a number of positions. When it does become so attached, the point of attachment determines where the ring will open. Once opened, the chromosome apparently remains as a rod.

Bacterial Viruses

Like bacteria and higher organisms, viruses, too, have genes. In fact, investigations of viruses have contributed and are contributing in important ways to our understanding of the nature of genetic information.

Viruses that parasitize bacteria have been especially useful for genetic study, especially those that multiply in the colon bacillus. These viruses are often called bacteriophages, or phages, or coliphages. Their role in modern genetics goes back about a quarter of a century. At that time a postdoctoral fellow, Emory Ellis, at the California Institute of Technology began a series of studies on the life cycle of a coliphage. He did this in his spare time, for he was committed to work on cancer in experimental animals. Bacterial viruses were then thought to be quite unrelated to cancer. In retrospect it is now clear that the virus work Ellis initiated has had a great deal more to do with understanding the nature of malignancy than anything he ever did directly on cancer cells as such.

While Ellis was developing quantitative methods for investigating bacterial viruses, Max Delbrück arrived from Germany to work at the California Institute of Technology as a Rockefeller Foundation Fellow. He was interested in new ways of finding out about genes. The bacterial viruses Ellis was studying looked to Delbrück like promising genetic material. The two men soon established a most fruitful collaboration.

It was not long before Ellis and Delbrück had worked out the important features of the viral life cycle and had developed techniques for quantitative studies that are now standard.

We now know that there are many related bacterial viruses capable of growing in the colon bacillus. All are submicroscopic. Among them is one called T4. A T4 virus consists of a polyhedral head some several hundred ängstrom units long with a tail-like projection of approximately equal length. The head consists of a coat of protein and a core of DNA. The latter consists of a single molecule of DNA made up of some 200,000 nucleotide pairs. The tail is protein with a central lumen stoppered at its tip with a protein plug.

During the process of infection, virus particles attach themselves to the bacterial host cell wall by the tips of their tails. Within a few minutes, the DNA core is injected into the host cell through the viral tail. One or many virus particles may infect a single host cell. Inside the host cell viral DNA is multiplied a hundredfold. Viral protein coats are synthesized by the host, intact daughter viral units are assembled and some twenty minutes after the initial infection the host cell bursts (undergoes lysis) with the release of some hundred or so daughter viruses. All may come from a single infecting particle, or if there were several original infecting particles the progeny will be a mixed brood.

A hundredfold or even greater increase per generation represents rapid reproduction indeed. If enough host cells were available and the travel time were reduced to zero, a single virus particle would give rise to something like 100^{71} progeny in twenty-four hours. This is far more than the total estimated number of elementary particles in the visible universe.

There are many kinds of bacterial viruses that multiply in colon bacilli. There are also many kinds of bacteria. Both viruses and bacteria are mutable. If one infects a large number of bacterial cells with an equally large number of viruses to which they are susceptible, some of the bacteria will be found to be resistant to the virus. They become resistant through mutation, presumably by changing the pattern of electrostatic charges on bacterial cell membrane. This is gene-determined. The change is a mutation. Such mutations occur spontaneously. They are not a response to the virus. They occur regularly at a low frequency. In the presence of a virulent virus, susceptible bacteria will be killed while resistant mutants will continue to multiply. It is possible with such a system of bacteria and viruses to make a lecture-table experiment showing that mutations with survival value will outgrow their nonmutant counterparts in a matter of an hour or less. If one now attempts to infect the resistant strain with the virus to which they are resistant, it can easily be shown that the virus too is mutable. Perhaps one in a million viruses in a population will mutate in such a way that it will now fit the pattern on the bacterium. In this case the mutant virus will rapidly replace the nonmutant viruses. But again there will be mutant bacteria resistant to the new virus. This is a never-ending process. The virus and the bacterium undergo constant change, each seemingly attempting to out-mutate the other. Neither side ever wins the battle permanently. Viruses that are changed in this respect are called host-range mutants.

If a dense suspension of bacteria infected with a few virus particles is plated on a Petri dish culture, the bacteria will overgrow the surface of the culture to form an opaque layer with clear circular areas wherever a virus particle lands. These circles of lysed bacteria produced by virus colonies are called plaques. The size and shape of such a plaque will depend on both the virus and the host. Both are mutable with respect to plaque characteristics. With such mutant viruses it is possible to demonstrate a kind of sexual process in the virus life cycle. If two virus particles differing from each other by two separate mutant genes simultaneously infect a single bacterial cell, it is found that not only do progeny like the two infecting viruses appear but two recombination types appear as well. One of these is a double mutant, the other carries no mutant gene at all. In this way it can be shown that mutation in the virus chromosome, consisting of a DNA molecule, involves a localized genetic change. There is a kind of mating process during which DNA molecules differing in two regions produce recombinant molecules. The frequency of such recombination depends on the distance between the two mutant genes.

This is essentially the way we study genes in higher organisms. The probability of recombination is a function of the distance apart of the two genes in the virus chromosome. If they are at opposite ends they recombine with a high frequency. If they are very close together they recombine with a low frequency. It is possible to construct genetic maps for viruses in much the same manner as that by which they are made for higher organisms.

It was pointed out earlier that, when a virus infects a bacterial cell, the virus injects its DNA, leaving the protein coat outside. How is this known? (Remember, the virus is submicroscopic.) The answer is, by means of radioactive labels in the DNA and protein virus components. This was first done by Hershey and Chase in 1952. Proteins contain sulphur but no phosphorus. DNA, on the other hand, contains phosphorus but no sulphur. So if one grows a virus culture on bacteria that had been grown in a medium containing radioactive sulphur—sulphur 35—the protein coat will be labeled. If such viruses are grown in bacteria without the label it is simple to determine whether the radioactivity stays outside or enters the host cell when infection occurs. The answer is clear. In this case very little of the labeled substance is found inside the cell. Most of it remains outside in the viral coats that can be removed by placing the infected bacteria in a Waring blender where the shearing forces knock the virus coats off in such a way that they can be separated from the cells in a centrifuge. The bacteria sediment at lower speeds than do the coats.

If a similar experiment is made with radioactive phosphorus, it can be shown that the labeled substance enters the host cell during infection. That is, DNA enters the host cell with very little protein. DNA labeled with P^{32} can be followed to a second generation of viruses. The small amount of protein that enters the host cell—presumably the tail plug—does not carry over as protein to a subsequent brood of viruses.

The conclusion is therefore clear that only DNA is carried over intact from one generation of viruses to the next.

Since viruses have genes and genes must be transmitted, it is obvious that viral genes must be DNA, or at least reducible to DNA at this one stage in the life cycle.

This viral DNA must carry specifications for making new viruses. It evidently takes over the metabolic machinery of the host cell, at least in part, and directs it to make viral DNA components and viral proteins.

There are other interesting facts about bacterial viruses and bacteria that I want to mention. In some bacterial viruses the DNA that enters the host cell establishes a so-called lysogenic state. The viral DNA somehow attaches itself to the bacterial chromosome, multiplies with it and does not result in lysis of the host cell. This viral DNA is transmitted from generation to generation of bacteria as a part of the genetic material of the host. It turns out that when this happens, the virus particles sometimes carry DNA from the host in which they matured, which they take with them into the bacterium with which they establish the lysogenic state. This carried-over bacterial DNA may replace its counterpart in the new host and change its genetic type. This phenomenon is called transduction. It provides a powerful genetic tool for studying bacterial genetics. If one has three very closely linked genes, say A, B, and C, in the bacterial chromosome in that order, and a small piece of DNA is carried over by the virus to the donor, it can replace either A, B, or C. Or it could replace A and B together, B and C, or all three. But there is one pair that cannot be replaced by a single DNA segment, namely, A and C without B. This, then, determines that B is in the middle of the sequence of three genes. This conclusion comes from the relative frequencies of the several possibilities for gene replacement. This has been called the "short blanket" technique. With such a blanket one can cover the feet and middle, the middle and head, but not the head and feet leaving the middle exposed—that is if one lies straight.

DNA as the Genetic Material

It is obvious that viruses have genes and that these must be DNA. It is clear, but not quite so obvious, that this is also true for bacteria. DNA is the genetic material, in a very real sense "the stuff of life." In 1952 this was clearly realized by many geneticists, including James Dewey Watson. Watson therefore decided that one of the most important problems of biology was the structure of DNA, for if this were known, one would know a great deal about how genetic specifications are written, how they are copied, how they are translated, and how they are modified by mutation. Watson thereupon went to Cambridge University to work with Francis H. C. Crick on the molecular structure of DNA.

To make a very important story very brief, within several months Watson and Crick had worked out a structure which looked as though it might well be essentially correct. The details of this structure and its implications will provide the basis for the second lecture in this series.

II. IN MOLECULAR TERMS

THE PREVIOUS LECTURE dealt with the background and some of the evidence for the conclusion that the primary genetic material in cellular forms and in some but not all viruses consists of molecules of deoxyribonucleic acid or DNA. Let us review the evidence briefly. Recall that one can transform a pneumococcus bacterium of one serological type to another by transferring nothing but pure DNA from donor to recipient. It is clear also, from the work of Hershey and Chase that in bacterial viruses the infective part of the virus is DNA. The protein coat is dispensable. This was first established by radioactive labeling of the two components. Since it is now possible to remove the protein and infect with naked DNA alone, it is abundantly clear that the only component that can carry genetic instructions from one generation to the next in these organisms is DNA. We cannot be so sure of this for higher organisms like ourselves, but for economy of hypothesis, we assume it is so. Our chromosomes are composed of DNA and proteins and we assume DNA is the primary genetic material.

Structure of DNA

I now turn to the question of molecular structure in DNA. The Watson-Crick structure of DNA, first proposed in 1953, is an elegant one chemically and physically. It also immediately suggested to its authors the answers to several basic questions geneticists ask about the material of heredity. In working out this structure, Watson and Crick had available a large amount of information on the chemical composition and the physical characteristics of DNA. DNA had first been isolated about a hundred years previously by the German chemist Miescher, who obtained it from fish sperm. Since then many investigators have added to our knowledge of it. For example, the structure of the four principal subunits or nucleotides was known in considerable detail. The relative proportions in which these four subunits occur were also known for a number of native DNA's. A group at King's College, London, including M. H. F. Wilkins, had done a great deal of work on DNA structure using x-ray diffraction techniques. By this means it was determined that the native DNA molecule has a helical structure. The proportions of the four nucleotides were such as to suggest that for every adenine nucleotide there was one thymine nucleotide. Likewise the guanine and cytosine nucleotides appeared to be in a one-to-one molar ratio.

All of this evidence, plus ingenious model-building by Watson and Crick, suggested that native DNA consisted of two chains of nucleotides running parallel, twisted in a double helix of uniform pitch and held together by hydrogen bonds between purine and pyrimidine components of paired nucleotides. The final model, schematically represented in figure 3, further suggested that the paired polynucleotide chains are complementary in nucleotide sequence, adenine always being specifically hydrogen-bonded to thymine and guanine to cytosine. In the paired chains the indivdual nucleotides are so oriented as to give the chains opposite polarity. The two chains are therefore said to be "antiparallel."

The structure proposed by Watson and Crick has proved to be essentially correct. The evidence comes from many

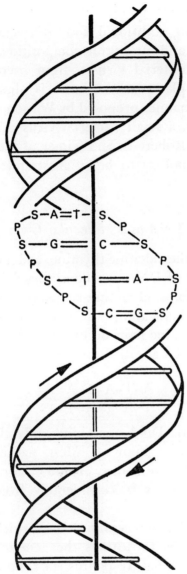

FIG. 3. The Watson-Crick structure of DNA schematically represented. The parallel spiral ribbons represent the paired polynucleotide chains. Hydrogen bonding is represented by transverse parallel lines. P = phosphate group. S = sugar unit. A = adenine base. T = thymine base. G = guahine base. C = cytosine base. Arrows indicate that polynucleotide chains run in opposite directions as specified by the sugar-phosphate linkages. (Redrawn from Watson and Crick, 1953.)

sources including additional x-ray diffraction data, radio-active labeling, and nucleotide composition.

DNA from bacterial viruses, from bacteria, and from several higher plants and animals is almost surely con-structed in the manner proposed by Watson and Crick. Re-cently, however, a small bacterial virus called ϕX174 has been shown by Robert L. Sinsheimer of the California In-stitute of Technology to be single-stranded, not double-stranded.

DNA as a Molecular Code

Structurally the adenine-thymine and guanine-cytosine nucleotide pairs of DNA can be arranged in the molecule in any proportion and in any sequence. Thus there are now known synthetic and possibly natural DNA's in which only adenine-thymine pairs occur. Designating these A:T, the two nucleotides alternate in the two chains as follows:

$$A–T–A–T–A–T–$$
$$T–A–T–A–T–A–$$

Likewise synthetic DNA containing only guanine-cytosine nucleotide pairs is known. Most naturally occurring DNA's, however, have both A:T and C:G nucleotide pairs in proportions that vary considerably from organism to organism.

DNA is a kind of molecular code in which the sequence of nucleotide pairs constitutes the genetically significant information. The nature of this code, now beginning to be understood, will be discussed later in connection with the use of genetic information.

Since DNA encodes a large part of our biological inher-itance as well as that of most other organisms, it is of inter-est to consider the amount of information carried in a

single cell, or in the head of a submicroscopic bacterial virus. Let us assume a coding system in which sequences of
three nucleotides represent letters of the alphabet. Since
a T4 bacterial virus particle contains 200,000 nucleotide
pairs, this is equivalent to about 70,000 letters. Assuming
five-letter words with a space for each word, these would
make about 12,000 words, or 24 printed pages of 500 words
each.

A similar calculation for the information carried in the
DNA molecules of a single human cell, first made by Crick,
indicates that the 5,000,000,000 nucleotide pairs are the
equivalent of 1,000 printed volumes of 500 words each, 600
pages per volume. If this amount of DNA were strung together in a single long molecule, it would be about five feet
long and about one ten-millionth of an inch in diameter.
Folded back and forth on the head of a pin so as to form a
solid film equal in thickness to the diameter of a DNA
double helix (20 ängstrom units), only about a two-hun-
dredth of the head of the pin would be covered. To cover
it completely would require about 200 such molecules, the
equivalent in information to 200,000 printed volumes of
the size previously indicated.

Stated another way, the DNA information required to
specify that a normal person will develop from a fertilized
human egg cell, given a proper environment and a quantitatively and qualitatively adequate supply of food, is the
equivalent of 1,000 printed volumes. That is the size of
the genetic recipe required to construct a person from the
egg cell.

Another way of dramatizing the miniaturization of information coded in DNA molecules: If the DNA of all the
human egg cells that have given rise to the present world
population, some three billion, were stacked neatly like
miniature cordwood, it would fit nicely into a tiny cubical

box one-eighth of an inch on a side, and there would be room to spare.

Cytoplasmic Information

Nuclear genetic information of the kind that has occupied the attention of classical geneticists is by no means the only hereditary information that is transmitted via the egg cell. We know that the cytoplasm of this cell is not only indispensable but also highly specific. This is clearly shown by experiments in which the nucleus of one genetic type is transferred to an enucleated egg of another. John Moore of Columbia University has shown that, if the nucleus of an egg of the frog *Rana pipiens* is replaced by its counterpart from *Rana sylvatica*, development fails at an early stage. Controls in which the nucleus of an egg is replaced by one from an egg of the same species show that the operation *per se*, delicate as it is, does not interfere with development. Clearly the cytoplasm and the nucleus must be compatible, which is another way of saying that the cytoplasm contains specific biological information necessary for development.

From experiments on the protozoan paramecium one can say somewhat more. Tracy Sonneborn has shown that cytoplasmic structures in this animal somehow serve as models for the construction of their replicas during cell division. Without the model no copy is formed. If the model is defective, the copy is likewise defective.

In addition to nuclear and cytoplasmic information, development of an organism requires raw material, in higher animals, in the form of food. In man food provides molecular building blocks as well as a source of energy. For a human egg to develop normally into an adult person, as much as 40,000 pounds of food may be required. Of course it must be of the right kind and it must be available at the right times and in the right amounts. Information is fed into the developing system in this way too.

DNA Replication

From fertilized egg to mature egg or sperm in man there occur many cell generations in the germ line, perhaps a dozen to several dozen, depending on age and sex. With each of these divisions, the total information coded in DNA must be copied. This is the equivalent of copying the content of the 1,000 standard volumes of 300,000 words each. It involves the assembling of perhaps 1,000,000,000,000,000 nucleotide units in proper sequence. Considering the opportunity for error, the copying mechanism must operate with truly amazing precision. How is it accomplished?

The answer was immediately suggested by the Watson-Crick structure. Since the paired antiparallel DNA chains are complementary in nucleotide sequence, each in a sense "knows" what its partner ought to be. Therefore, if the two chains were to separate, each could be expected to serve as a template against which a complementary partner could be constructed. This can be illustrated by a segment of four nucleotide pairs represented by the four initial letters of the identifying purines and pyrimidines, thus:

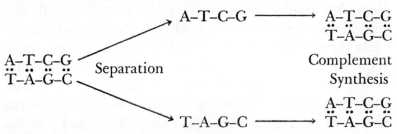

The conditions within the cell that bring about opening of the weak hydrogen bonds are not understood. It is known, however, that double-stranded DNA in solution is separated into its component single strands by heating under appropriate conditions. Slow cooling results in reunion of the pairs.

In a cell in which DNA replication occurs, the component nucleotides required for replication are synthesized through normal metabolic processes, ultimately from components of food in our own species. The proper ordering of the units of the daughter chains is presumably determined by the hydrogen-bond patterns and dimensional considerations.

This is the hypothesis originally proposed by Watson and Crick. It is a most elegant hypothesis. The question immediately arises: Is it correct? There are several ways of testing it. One is by use of isotopic labeling of DNA chains in such a way that old chains differ detectably from new ones. By means of an ingenious method of measuring small differences in buoyant density, it is possible to separate, identity, and measure small amounts of DNA in an analytical ultracentrifuge. Essentially this consists in dissolving cell materials in a cesium chloride solution of appropriate concentration. When such a solution mixture is spun in an analytical centrifuge, the cesium chloride molecules form a density gradient by establishing an equilibrium between sedimentation and back diffusion. In such a gradient, DNA molecules at the top of the centrifuge cell (centripetal end) sink until they reach a region of equal density, while those at the bottom of the cell (centrifugal end) float to the same density level. In this way DNA molecules form a sharp band across the cell at their isodensity level. Other molecules, being of different densities, either sink to the bottom of the cell or float to the top. The band position of DNA is determined by an ultraviolet optical system. The band is sharp because DNA molecules are large and diffuse very slowly. Their position indicates density. The amount of DNA is determined by the amount of ultraviolet absorption. The distribution of DNA in the band is a function of both molecular weight and size-homogeneity in the population of DNA modecules. Thus, with a relatively simple technique it is possible to measure density of DNA, amount, and molecular weight.

With this method, developed by M. S. Meselson, F. W. Stahl, and J. Vinograd, it became possible easily to test the Watson-Crick hypothesis of DNA replication. This was done with the colon bacillus by labeling all DNA with heavy nitrogen atoms, N^{15} instead of N^{14}. Bacteria were grown in a culture medium containing only N^{15} for several generations until the seven and eight nitrogen atoms in the two base pairs were all of the heavy isotope. This increases the molecular weight and density of DNA by about one per cent. This "heavy" DNA forms a band in the ultracentrifuge tube at a different position from its "light" counterpart containing only N^{14}. Thus, if equal parts of heavy and light DNA are mixed and banded in the centrifuge, there are two distinct and clearly separated bands.

The Meselson-Stahl test was carried out as follows: bacteria containing heavy DNA only were washed to free them from external culture medium. They were then grown in a culture medium containing only light nitrogen (N^{14}). If the Watson-Crick hypothesis is correct and the two single strands of DNA retain their linear integrity during replication, then after one cell division, as determined by the doubling of the bacterial population in the experimental cultures, all bacterial cells should contain DNA molecules consisting of one heavy and one light chain. They should be exactly intermediate in density between N^{15} heavy and N^{14} light DNA. This was found to be the case.

After a second generation, as determined by a second

doubling of the cell number, half the DNA molecules should be half-heavy (one chain containing N^{15}, the other N^{14}) and the other light (both chains containing only N^{14}). Again the result predicted on the basis of the simple form of the Watson-Crick hypothesis was obtained.

This is rather persuasive evidence in favor of the hypothesis. But it is not final proof, for there might be other mechanisms that would give the observed results in this type of experiment. Confirming and even more convincing evidence comes from the work of Arthur Kornberg and co-workers. Kornberg set out to see whether he could devise an *in vitro* system in which DNA would replicate as it does in a living cell. Most biochemists at the time were of the opinion that the process must be so complex that the chance of getting it to go on in a test tube was so exceedingly small that it was scarcely worth attempting. But the Kornberg group succeeded.

They demonstrated that DNA molecules added in a test tube to a solution containing the four nucleotide components of DNA as triphosphates (two phosphate groups per nucleotide in addition to the one present in the final DNA molecule), with a suitable buffer solution of inorganic salts, magnesium ions, and a specific enzyme capable of catalyzing the polymerization of nucleotides, will cause more DNA molecules to be formed. The "primer" DNA molecules appeared to be replicated.

Is the newly formed DNA in such a system like the primer? The evidence suggests strongly that it is. DNA's from different organisms differ in their ratios of adenine-thymine to cytosine-guanine nucleotide pairs. The newly formed DNA in the Kornberg system has the same ratio as the primer.

Some time after these first experiments were carried out, it was found that DNA molecules may be formed in the

Kornberg system *without DNA molecules being added.*
Such spontaneously formed DNA does not appear immediately as does that synthesized in response to a primer but
only after a lag period of a few hours.

Depending on the circumstances, this spontaneously
formed DNA may consist of only adenine-thymine base
pairs alternating in the double chain in the following manner:

$$A-T-A-T-A-T-A-T-$$
$$T-A-T-A-T-A-T-A-$$

If this A:T co-polymer is now used as a primer in a new
system, more DNA is immediately synthesized and *it is of
the A:T co-polymer type of the primer.*

Under somewhat different conditions a second type of
DNA appears spontaneously in the absence of primer.
This consists solely of guanine-cytosine base pairs arranged
as follows:

$$C-C-C-C-C-$$
$$G-G-G-G-G-$$

Again, if this C:G synthetic DNA is used as a primer,
more of the same C:G DNA is formed without delay.

Collectively, these several lines of investigation add up
to powerful and convincing evidence that the simple Watson-Crick hypothesis is essentially correct, at least in the
living bacterial cell and in the Kornberg test-tube system.

What about higher forms in which DNA is organized in
an as yet not fully understood way in chromosomes? Here
too there is evidence that the hypothesis is correct. J. Her-
bert Taylor and associates have followed the replication of
DNA in higher plant and animal cells by labeling DNA
molecules with the radioactive isotope of DNA hydrogen-3
or tritium. If the tritium label is followed by radioauto-

graphic methods in which the labeled chromosomes are allowed to register their presence on radiosensitive photographic film, it is found that the DNA molecules behave as predicted. Labeled chromosomes are permitted to replicate in the absence of label. The daughter chromosomes are labeled as expected, but granddaughter chromosome segments are either labeled or unlabeled as though in this generation the labeled DNA chains were cleanly separated from their unlabeled partners just as they are in the Meselson-Stahl experiment.

What about the single-stranded DNA of the bacterial virus ϕX174? It has been shown that in its replication it first acquires a complementary partner, both when it replicates in a living bacterial cell and when it replicates in the Kornberg system.

Translation of DNA Specifiications

We have already considered some of the evidence showing that genes determine specificities in proteins, those active as enzymes in particular. How is this translation carried out? Fortunately, the main outlines of this basic biological process have been exposed.

Let us begin with the assumption that a specific protein is determined by a segment of DNA that we call a gene. Since protein specificity depends on the sequence of its amino-acid building blocks, of which there are twenty kinds, there must be some coding relation between the sequence of the four nucleotides of the gene and the twenty amino acids of the corresponding protein. It is now known that in cellular forms the translation involves an intermediate information-carrying molecule, namely, ribonucleic acid (RNA).

RNA, like DNA, is a linear polymer built up of a sequence of nucleotides much like those found in DNA. Ribonucleotides differ from those of DNA in having one more oxygen atom in each ribose sugar component. The thymine nucleotide of DNA is replaced by a uridine nucleotide in RNA. Otherwise, adenine, cytosine, and guanine deoxynucleotides in DNA are represented by adenine, cytosine, and guanine ribonucleotides in RNA. If we distinguish RNA nucleotides from those of DNA by representing the former in italicized abbreviations, an A–T–C–G-sequence of DNA would correspond to an $A–U–C–G$-sequence in RNA.

RNA is capable of assuming a double helical structure much like that of DNA. A four-unit segment of such a double chain of RNA would then be represented as:

$$A–U–C–G–$$
$$U–A–G–C–$$

Hybrid DNA-RNA molecules in which one chain is DNA and its partner is RNA are possible. They would be represented as:

$$A–T–C–G–$$
$$U–A–G–C–$$

It has been demonstrated by Samuel Weiss and others that the transfer of DNA nucleotide sequence from DNA to RNA can occur in a cell-free solution in the test tube, presumably by a template mechanism of this kind.

It is presumed that what happens *in vivo* is that specific RNA molecules are copied from DNA in the nucleus by such a template mechanism. Thus from the DNA segment that constitutes the gene for specifying the alpha protein chain of hemoglobin [1] is copied an RNA molecule of cor-

---

[1] Hemoglobin molecules contain two kinds of protein chains, called alpha and beta, two of each per molecule. Each of the four chains is made up of about 150 amino-acid residues.

responding specificity. This is called messenger RNA. Messenger RNA moves from the nucleus to the cytoplasm of the cell, where it becomes incorporated or associated with one or more submicroscopic structure called ribosomes. Here it acts as a template against which amino acids are arranged in the sequence characteristic of the alpha chain of the hemoglobin molecule. On completion the newly synthesized protein separates from the ribosome and is incorporated in an intact hemoglobin molecule.

How do the twenty kinds of amino acids find their proper position against the messenger RNA template? Each of the twenty kinds is tagged by being enzymatically attached to a specific small RNA molecule, which is called transfer RNA. There are twenty kinds of transfer RNA molecules, each specific to a particular amino acid. There are also twenty specific enzymes that attach the twenty amino acids to their corresponding transfer RNA molecules.

Transfer RNA molecules are believed to be about 80 nucleotides in length, folded back on themselves hairpinlike with the two arms joined in complementary fashion by hydrogen bonds and twisted in a double helix like a DNA molecule. Amino acids are attached to the end of the molecule opposite the turn. Three unpaired nucleotides in the region of the turn are presumed to be the coding unit.

As each transfer RNA-amino acid complex comes into contact with messenger RNA, the transfer RNA coding unit specifically attaches itself to a complementary three-nucleotide coding unit of the messenger template. In this way the various amino acids are lined up according to the sequence of coding units of the template. Enzymatic formation of peptide linkages joins the amino acids to form a protein molecule which then separates from the template and leaves the ribosome complex.

Not only can the replication of DNA be carried out *in*

vitro but so can the synthesis of DNA-directed RNA, presumably messenger RNA.

Likewise the synthesis of specific proteins can be observed in a test-tube system containing messenger RNA, ribosomes, amino acids, amino acid-activating enzymes, and a polypeptidase. It has even been determined in such systems that amino acids are polymerized in sequence beginning at the free-amino end of the protein chain.

In 1961 Nirenberg and Matthaei made the remarkable discovery that RNA's synthesized in a test-tube system in which no DNA is present to specify the sequence of nucleotides can serve as messenger RNA. Thus an RNA containing only uracil nucleotides (poly-U RNA) serves to direct the synthesis of a polypeptide containing only the amino acid phenylalanine. This finding led to the conclusion that the RNA coding unit for this amino acid is *U–U–U*. The corresponding DNA sequence specifying this coding unit would then be A–A–A.

By using artificial messenger RNA's made up of other combinations and proportions of the four component nucleotides, it has been possible to determine the coding units for all twenty amino acids normally found in proteins. The sequence of nucleotides in the coding unit for the amino acid tyrosine has been determined in Severo Ochoa's laboratory by using an artificial messenger RNA made up of uracil nucleotides except for a single terminal adenine nucleotide, thus:

$$. . . –U–U–U–U–A$$

The polypeptide synthesized with this messenger RNA consists of phenylalanine except for the carboxyl terminal amino acid, which is tyrosine. It is therefore concluded that the RNA code for tyrosine is *U–U–A* in that sequence. As we shall see later, other coding units can be deduced from mutational changes which lead to the substitution of one amino acid to another.

In the foregoing discussion we have assumed that the amino-acid coding units of DNA and RNA are sequences of three nucleotides, that is, that the DNA "words" signifying specific amino acids are "three-letter" words. How do we know this? To answer this question we shall first have to consider the nature of gene mutation.

Gene Mutation

In proposing the structure of DNA described here, Watson and Crick proposed that gene mutations consisted in changes in nucleotide sequence. They further proposed that one way in which these could come about is through mistakes in the replicative process. Thus if in the synthesis of complementary partner chains by single-stranded DNA templates an adenine nucleotide should select a cytosine partner, instead of the normal thymine partner, there would be formed an $A:C$ pair instead of the normal $A:T$ pair. In the next round of replication the C nucleotide would be expected to select its proper G partner. Thus a $G:C$ pair would replace an $A:T$ pair. This might occur as a result of the original A nucleotide existing in a rare tautomeric form such that it would hydrogen-bond with C instead of T.

We now know that nitrites will specifically oxidize NH_2 groups to OH groups in nucleotides and thus modify their hydrogen-bonding specificities. The fact is that nitrites do produce mutations, presumably in this way. Artificially modified nucleotides can be supplied a living organism in such a way that they are incorporated in DNA. Here again the specific hydrogen-bonding pattern may be modified in a way that increases the chance of error in replication. Such mutations are known to occur. Acridine dyes are mutagenic and there is evidence that they act by causing single nucleotides to be added or deleted from a DNA molecule during replication. High-energy radiation is also known to be mutagenic, by either directly or indirectly modifying nucleotides of DNA.

From these various lines of evidence and from genetic studies, we believe mutations can be of four kinds, namely (1) addition, (2) subtraction, (3) substitution, (4) inversion of nucleotides, or (5) more complex rearrangements. In some respects they are like typographical errors in a typed or printed message.

We are all familiar with the code in which our language is written. It can be written equally well in a twenty-six-symbol code, the letters of the alphabet, or in a two-symbol code, dots and dashes. Obviously, many other codes could be and have been devised for conveying the same information. The DNA-RNA code is "written" in four symbols, i.e. nucleotides. It is a linear code like our language, but it differs in that there are no spaces between coding units. Thus in the RNA sequence $U–U–U–A–U–G–U–U–A \ldots$, we read successive triplets of nucleotides to give the three-"letter" words UUU, AUG and UUA. These specify the three amino acids phenylalanine, glutamic acid, and tyrosine.

That this concept is highly probable was shown by Crick *et al.* in studying a whole series of acridine-induced mutations in one of the genes of the bacterial virus T4. They were able to classify these into two groups, one assumed to involve additions of single nucleotides, the other to involve omissions of single nucleotides.

In a message determining the sequence of amino acids in a protein, either the addition or the subtraction of a single nucleotide near the end of the molecule from which the message is read (what determines where a given protein specification begins and ends is not known) will obviously modify all or most all subsequent triplets and thus lead to the formation of a greatly altered protein, or, more likely, scramble the directions so greatly that no protein at all is possible. But if we induce two mutations, one an addition and the other an omission, the two will compensate and the bulk of the message will be unaltered and will likely specify a functional protein. If two additions or two subtractions are made near the beginning of the message, the subsequent triplets will be scrambled. However, if either three nucleotides are omitted or three added near the beginning of the message, sense will be made of the remainder of the message.

Crick *et al.* found these relations to hold for many mutations in the particular gene they investigated. The assumption that the code involved is a space-free triplet code in which successive triplets but not the overlapping triplets are read is consistent with these findings.

Mutations Leading to Single Amino-Acid Substitution

Obviously, many mutations in which a single nucleotide is substituted by another will lead to proteins in which one amino acid is replaced by another. These are sometimes called "missense" mutations. Thus, in the sequence

$$- - - U\ U\ A - - - \dots$$

the UUA triplet will specify tyrosine. If by mutation *UUA* is changed to *UUU*, phenylalanine will replace tyrosine in the final protein. On the other hand, if the change is from *UUA* to *UAA*, the amino acid specified by the original triplet will be omitted without replacement, for the triplet *UAA* appears not to encode any of the twenty amino acids. This is sometimes called a "nonsense" mutation.

A large number of single-gene mutations in a variety of organisms ranging all the way from viruses to man have been described in terms of such single amino-acid substitutions in specific proteins. Thus in hemoglobin in man, we know that the sickel-cell mutation results in a replacement of glutamic acid in a specific position in the beta chain of hemoglobin by valine. In C hemoglobin, the same glutamic acid is replaced by lysine. Dozens of similar cases could be cited. Presumably in this way the sequences of all three-symbol coding units for the twenty amino acids will be determined before too long.

Fine Structure

Assuming a triplet code, it is obvious that a segment of DNA of not less than 450 nucleotides is necessary to specify the sequence of the 150 amino acids in the beta chain of human hemoglobin. If what we have said up to now is correct, it should follow that a change in any one of these 450 nucleotides which constitute the gene for the beta chain will lead to mutation unless the code is "degenerate" in the sense that more than one triplet sequence can specify a single amino acid. Actually, there is evidence suggesting that there may exist degeneracy of this kind in the DNA code.

But regardless of whether the code is degenerate or not, it is obvious that mutations at many positions in the gene are possible. Again this has been demonstrated to be the case for many individual genes. The work of Seymour Benzer on the so-called rII mutants of bacterial virus T4 demonstrates this in a spectacular way, for in this organism intragenic crossing over is easy to demonstrate and measure quantitatively. As a result, a linear map of the mutational sites within the rII gene can be demonstrated. In fact the lowest observable level of intragenic recombination is of the order expected for that between adjacent nucleotides.

Perhaps even more remarkably, Charles Yanofsky and his collaborators have shown that genetic recombination occurs within a single coding unit designating an amino acid in a specific position in a known protein. Thus in the heterozygote $\frac{UUG}{UGC}$ in which UUG specifies valine amino acid and UGC specifies arginine, the recombinations UUC and UGG have been identified which correspond to serine and glycine amino acids respectively. Note that RNA triplets are specified. Recombination of course occurs in the DNA triplets that specify these.

Let me summarize by pointing out that the DNA-RNA system appears to be the universal "language" in which specifications for all living systems are written. It is a language written in an alphabet of but four "letters." All the "words" consist of but three letters and there are only sixty-four words possible.

Biology in its most basic molecular aspects has turned out to be amazingly simple.

III.   EVOLUTION AND THE NATURE OF MAN

W E BELIEVE a large part of organic evolution is the result of changes in DNA specifications of living systems.   We must be careful, however, not to say that *all*
evolution depends on such change, for, as I have pointed
out in a previous lecture, the cytoplasm also carries information from one generation to the next in cellular organisms.

To review the nature of DNA information, the manner
in which this is used in protein synthesis and some characteristics of mutation, let us now designate the four nucleotides of DNA by four frequently used letters of the modern
European alphabet, NEAT.   With a bit of poetic license,
we can make twenty meaningful three-letter words with
these.   Just for purposes of illustration I shall assume that
these are the twenty code words designating the twenty
amino acids.   Now I write the message:

ANNTATNANNETEENTANANTNATTENNAT
AENANTATETNTNATTEANATTEENAEANT.

Without knowing the convention for reading a DNA message, this message does not appear to make much sense.   If,
however, we add spaces so as to make the three-letter words
obvious and add punctuation marks at appropriate points,
we get the following: ANN TAT.   NAN NET EEN TAN
ANT, NAT TEN, NAT AEN.   ANT ATE TNT, NAT
TEA, NAT TEE.   NAE ANT.   Or, replacing the un-
familiar three-letter words with commonly used words, the
message reads: ANN TATTED.   NAN NETTED ONE
TAN ANT, NOT TEN, NOT A COPPER-COLORED

49

(AENEUS) ANT. (THE) ANT ATE TNT, NOT TEA, NOT TEE. NO ANT!

Going back to the original words, let us pretend that they encode the twenty amino acids as follows:

AEN	1	EAT	6	NAN	11	TAT	16
AET	2	EAN	7	NAT	12	TEA	17
ANN	3	EEN	8	NET	13	TEE	18
ANT	4	ETA	9	TAE	14	TEN	19
ATE	5	NAE	10	TAN	15	TNT	20

The original message would specify a protein with the amino acid sequence as follows:

3	16	11	13	8	15	4	12	19
ANN	TAT	NAN	NET	EEN	TAN	ANT	NAT	TEN

12	1	4	5	20	12	17	12	18
NAT	AEN	ANT	ATE	TNT	NAT	TEA	NAT	TEE

10	4
NAE	ANT

Let us now imagine possible mutations. First assume the omission of the third letter of the first word—the counterpart of the deletion of a nucleotide in a DNA message. We would now read:

ANT ATN ANN ETE ENT ANA NTH . . .

corresponding to the amino-acid sequence

4 – 3 – – – – . . .

Only two of the first seven words encode amino acids. Obviously such a mutant completely alters the message.

Adding a letter, say T, after the first three-letter word in the altered message gives:

ANT TAT NAN NET EEN TAN ANT . . .

which specifies the amino acid sequence

$$4 \quad 16 \quad 11 \quad 13 \quad 8 \quad 15 \quad 4 \ . \ . \ .$$

Except for the first word and the corresponding first amino acid, this second mutation restores the original message. Two successive deletions of single letters near the starting point of the message would, of course, not do this. Neither would two additions. But omission of three letters near the beginning of the message would restore all words to the right of the rightmost addition.

ANN NAN NET EEN TAN . . .

As mentioned in the previous lecture, it was the establishment of facts of a similar nature that led Crick and collaborators to conclude that DNA coding units consist of successive sets of three nucleotides.

I should now like to consider mutations of the kind that replace one nucleotide by another. In the above alphabetic analogy, let us consider the sixth word in the original message

ANN TAT NAN NET EEN TAN ANT . . .

Through all possible substitutions of single letters for T, A, and N in the word TAN we can derive the following nine triplets:

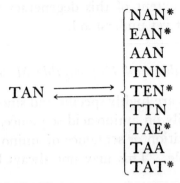

$$TAN \rightleftharpoons \left\{ \begin{array}{l} NAN^* \\ EAN^* \\ AAN \\ TNN \\ TEN^* \\ TTN \\ TAE^* \\ TAA \\ TAT^* \end{array} \right.$$

Referring back to the list of three-letter words, we see that TAN can mutate to any of five words, marked with asterisks, that make sense as words, or in the analogy, in encoding amino acids. These are called "missense" mutations. They make sense, but it is different sense from the original. The remaining four triplets do not make sense at all, either as *words* or as amino-acid coding triplets. These are called "nonsense" mutations. Of course, nonsense triplets can mutate back to the original or to missense triplets by further single-unit changes. Thus AAN can mutate to the original or to four new usable coding units as follows:

$$TAN \longleftarrow AAN \longrightarrow \begin{cases} AEN \\ ANN \\ EAN \\ NAN \end{cases}$$

In addition four nonsense mutants are possible.

Degeneracy in the Code

The above analysis of the English three-letter-word analogy with the DNA code assumes that the code is not "degenerate," that is, that a single amino acid is encoded by only one DNA triplet. Actually, there is increasingly persuasive evidence that the DNA-RNA code is in fact degenerate. The extent of this degeneracy and its full significance are not yet understood.

Favorable and Unfavorable Mutations

Since proteins are highly specific and since this specificity depends primarily on amino-acid sequence, mutations that alter the composition or sequence of amino acids are likely to be unfavorable. This may not always be so, however, for Henning and Yanofsky have shown that replacement of the amino acid glycine by alanine or serine does not produce easily detectable changes in the catalytic properties of a protein concerned with the synthesis of the amino acid tryptophane in the colon bacillus. It may be, however, that the proteins modified in this way may *in vivo* confer disadvantages too subtle to detect by the experimental methods used.

Some dozen or so mutations are known in man in which the hemoglobin molecule is altered. The first of these to be analyzed in terms of structure is the one that results in the production of sickle-cell hemoglobin, so named because red blood cells containing exclusively sickle-cell or "S" hemoglobin are distorted at low oxygen levels, often assuming the shape of a sickle.

Sickle-cell hemoglobin differs from normal hemoglobin in that the glutamic amino acids in specific positions in the two identical beta protein chains of the molecule are replaced by the amino acid valine.

Persons carrying two genes specifying S hemoglobin, which means they received the S from the specifying gene from both parents and are homozygous, suffer a severe type of hemolytic anemia. Without careful medical attention, including blood transfusions during critical periods, such persons rarely live to produce offspring. Heterozygotes for the S gene, that is, those carrying a normal form of this gene from one parent and an S mutant form from the other, suffer slight anemia only. Their red blood cells contain normal and S hemoglobin molecules in approximately equal numbers. Their oxygen-carrying capacity is reduced and they therefore do not make good mountain climbers or parachute jumpers.

It would seem clear that the mutation responsible for S hemoglobin is an unfavorable one. Under "normal" circumstances it clearly is. But there appears to be a special situation in which it is not. This involves populations living in areas in which falciparum malaria is endemic. There is evidence indicating that persons heterozygous for the sickle-cell gene, and who have both sickle-cell and normal hemoglobin, resist the parasitic plasmodium that causes the disease. Hence in such areas, parts of equatorial Africa for example, it seems clearly advantageous to be a carrier (heterozygote) of the S mutant gene. Accordingly as high as forty per cent of some populations under such conditions have the sickle-cell trait (are heterozygous for the S gene). The population cannot become one hundred per cent resistant, for a wholly heterozygous population, if somehow established, will give rise to homozygous normals (susceptible to malaria), homozygotes for S hemoglobin (who rarely survive) and heterozygotes in the Mendelian ratio $1:1:2$. Under these conditions the heterozygous state is the only obvious compromise that avoids the dilemma of either malaria or sickle-cell anemia.

In the absence of malaria, one would expect the S gene to be selected against, and so it seems to be. The incidence of the sickle-cell trait and anemia among descendants of equatorial African Negroes from malarial regions, now living in the United States, has dropped as expected, allowing for the additional decrease expected on the basis of racial mixture with populations in which there is almost no S hemoglobin.

The Environmental and Genetic Contexts

It is clear that a mutation need not be favorable or unfavorable in an absolute sense. Which it is will depend on both its environmental and its genetic contexts.

Consider first the environmental context. The S hemo-

globin mutation is a clear case in point. Penicillin resistance in some bacteria is another. In the micrococcus that
causes boils and sometimes more serious generalized infec-
tions, a mutation conferring resistance to penicillin is obviously a highly favorable one *in an environment in which
penicillin is present*. Otherwise the bacterium is unable
to reproduce. But *in the absence of penicillin* this same
mutation is unfavorable, for under these conditions the
penicillin-susceptible form reproduces faster than its resistant counterpart and soon almost completely replaces it
through *natural selection*.

At this point I might pause to indicate the rapidity with
which a form with a selective advantage may replace a
competing form. Take the bacterial case just mentioned
and assume that in the absence of penicillin the susceptible
type reproduces just rapidly enough to maintain a constant
population. This means that in each generation one bacterium dies without reproducing, while its sister lives to
reproduce. Assume that the resistant one doubles each
generation and that the generation time in each case is one
hour. After one hour the resistant type will outnumber
the susceptible form two to one. In ten hours—ten generations—the fast-growing one will have increased one thou-
sandfold, while the number of its resistant mutant counterpart will have remained constant. In twenty hours the
favored form will outnumber the slower one by a million
to one.

In two human populations initially equal in numbers,
with a similar difference in net reproductive rates, the more
rapidly reproducing population will increase a millionfold
in approximately six hundred years, while the slower one
will remain constant in size. For all practical purposes, the
one will have completely replaced the other. Of course
this assumes that the postulated differential rate of repro-

duction is maintained for twenty generations, a rather un-
likely but not inconceivable state of affairs in human populations.

Turning now to the genetic context in which a gene
mutation occurs, it is easy to show that here again "favorable" and "unfavorable" have meaning only in terms of
other components of the total genetic specifications.   In
the message

$\uparrow$

ANN TAT NAN NET EEN TAN ANT . . . ,

it is clear that omission of the N marked with an upward
arrow will lead to a scrambling of the message as follows:

ANT ATN ANN ETE ENT ANA NT . . .

This is clearly an unfavorable mutation.   But if prior to
this there had occurred a mutation change adding an A at
the position of the downward arrow to give the message

$\downarrow$

ANN ATA TNA NNE TEE NTA NANT . . . ,

also clearly unfavorable to the sense of the message, then
omission of the same N that was originally unfavorable now
becomes favorable as follows:

ANA TAT NAN NET EEN TAN ANT . . .

Aside from a change in the first triplet word, the message is
now restored to its original sense.

Whether a given gene mutation is favorable or unfavorable is analogous to the question of whether a given word
in a written message is favorable or unfavorable.   For example, the word "NOT" may be favorable in one context
such as "he will not die" and unfavorable in another such
as "he will not live."

The Typist Analogy

Evolution through mutation and natural selection can perhaps be made somewhat clearer by an analogy. Imagine a typist who types copy, as DNA copies itself, in a purely mechanical way. She does not read for sense either the material she types from or the copy she makes from it. She does not proofread it and she does not correct mistakes. She makes copies serially from a single original message, that is, makes one copy, copies the copy, copies the second copy, and so on indefinitely. Assume that she starts with a perfect copy of the Gettysburg Address and types one thousand copies in succession as described above. Assume also that she makes one typographical error, on the average, each time she types the total address. Clearly under these circumstances errors will accumulate, one each typing generation, so that after one thousand typings there will have occurred something like one thousand errors. Since the Gettysburg Address contains a total of some 1,150 letters, it is clear that the final copy will be reduced to nonsense. An occasional error might conceivably be favorable in the total context but surely most will be unfavorable, just as random mutations in a highly selected and well-adjusted organism are much more likely to be unfavorable than favorable.

Just as the Gettysburg Address would degenerate into nonsense through typographical errors, so too would our inherited structure degenerate over many generations if there were not some preventive mechanism. There is such a mechanism in organisms. We call it *natural selection.*

In the typist analogy we can add a procedure that does more or less what natural selection does in organic evolution. Suppose we add a proofreading supervisor. Each time the Gettysburg Address is typed the supervisor checks it. If there is an error, he throws the copy away and directs the typist to recopy the original. If there are no errors, he directs her to make a second copy from the first typing. Thus after one thousand successive copies have been produced and passed the final will be exactly like the original. The price paid for perfection will be the discarded copies. The supervisor is analogous to natural selection.

This is what happens with organisms. Copies of specifications containing unfavorable errors or mutations are discarded. The analogy is not perfect, for in organisms the unfavorable specifications may be discarded only over a number of generations by reducing below the average the number of offspring of individuals carrying the unfavorable mutation.

The analogy is faulty in another respect. It assumes that there are no favorable typographical errors. Although it is difficult to imagine typographical errors that would improve the Gettysburg Address, assume they are possible. Let us now change the instructions to the supervisor so that he will approve any copy with a favorable error. Under these conditions the Gettysburg Address will evolve into something better, at least in the judgment of the supervisor.

Clearly if the Gettysburg Address were less good to begin with, the opportunity for improvement through favorable errors would be greater. The same is true with organisms. The better adapted they are, the lower the probability that a given mutation will be favorable. If the environment changes, the chance that mutations will be favorable will of course increase.

Evolution by Small Mutations

It is conceivable and even probable that evolution occurs mostly through the slow accumulation of small mutations, that is, single-unit changes in RNA or DNA, that are favorable in the genetic and environmental contexts in which they occur. It is difficult to imagine any organism that could not have arisen from an ancestral form differing by a single mutational step. On the other hand, we cannot exclude the possibility that a complex of mutational changes might occasionally occur at a given time in a manner that would confer a selective advantage on the organisms that carried them all. An extreme form of this view was once put forward by the late Richard Goldschmidt. It has been called the "hopeful monster" hypothesis. He suggested that in this way a complex of mutational changes might occasionally occur together in such a way as to give rise to a new phylum in a single generation, for example, birds from reptiles. Most biologists do not take this hypothesis seriously, for they think it highly improbable that such mutational explosions would give rise to viable new organisms, especially when one realizes that in higher animals two of opposite sex are required to occur simultaneously. Such an assumption is considered quite unnecessary to account for evolution.

Working backward in evolutionary history, we suppose that modern man originated from a more primitive human form, he in turn from a pre-man, and so on through less specialized mammals, to relatively simple multicellular animals, to single-celled animals, to single-celled plants, to subcellular organisms like large viruses, to simpler viruses, to nucleic acid and protein molecules, to simpler "organic" molecules, to inorganic molecules, to the larger, more complex chemical elements, and, finally, to the simplest of all elements, hydrogen. The point is that once started on this quest for our origins, there is no logical place to stop short of the simplest system we can conceive, namely, a universe composed solely of hydrogen.

What are the reasons for assuming such an evolutionary

sequence? Starting with the hydrogen atom, nuclear physicists know that under favorable conditions of temperature and pressure—in the interior of the sun, for example—hydrogen will "burn" to helium. By a series of nuclear reactions, some of which are known experimentally and all of which appear reasonable in principle to nuclear physicists and cosmologists, all the known elements can and presumably do arise from hydrogen. These interact in known ways to give molecules such as those of hydrogen (H_2) containing two hydrogen atoms each, water (H_2O) made up of two hydrogens and one oxygen atom, ammonia (NH_3), methane (CH_4), and so on to molecules of increasing size and complexity.

The Origin of Life

Under appropriate conditions inorganic molecules interact to give "organic" molecules, so called because in the early days of chemistry it was believed that they arose only in living organisms. We know now that this is not so. For example, Stanley Miller and others have shown that a mixture of hydrogen, water, ammonia, and methane, four simple inorganic molecules, in a tube through which an electric spark is passed, interacts to form a series of amino acids such as glycine (CH_2NH_2COOH), alanine ($CH_3CH_2NH_2COOH$), and others. Such a reducing atmosphere almost surely occurred generally on earth several billion years ago; if not generally, then certainly locally.

Amino acids are known to interact under conditions of high temperature to give protein-like macromolecules. Chemists know how to synthesize small protein molecules *in vitro* from such macromolecules. Chemists also know how to synthesize the nucleotide building-blocks of nucleic acids and how to put them together to make RNA and DNA. Thus, as already said, Kornberg and co-workers have made artificial DNA molecules that replicate like natural DNA. Likewise, Ochoa and others have made artificial RNAs that serve like their natural counterparts in protein synthesis.

Chemists cannot make chemical reactions "go" that will not also go without them. True, they can arrange for favorable circumstances and thus increase the probability of a given reaction going. But any set of circumstances that can be arranged by the chemist conceivably somewhere sometime occurred in his absence. It follows therefore that favorable circumstances must have come about on earth for the formation of proteins, nucleic acids, combinations of proteins and nucleic acids like simple viruses.

I wish to point out that the origin of "life" in this way need not be thought of as a chance event. Given the right sequence of circumstances, it was as inevitable as the reactions arranged for by the chemist and which he regards as entirely predictable. The distinction between a "chance" event and a predictable and inevitable one is merely a difference in degree of probability. If the probability of an event happening in a time span measured in days is 0.001, that is, one in a thousand, we are inclined to call it a chance event. But if the probability is raised to 0.999, or 999 in 1,000, for the same time, we regard it as almost certain. Thus if for the event with the 0.001 probability of happening within a twenty-four hour period, we increase the time span to three million years, a very short time in terms of the age of the earth and the evolution of its living systems, the probability begins to approach certainty.

Increasing Opportunity

A point of considerable significance in the assumed sequence of evolutionary advances just discussed is the rapid increase in alternative pathways with increasing complexity of the system. Hydrogen alone has a limited immediate evolutionary outlook. Through neutron absorption it may change to H_2, H_3, H_4, or H_5. Its nuclei can and do fuse to form helium nuclei. These and the formation of simple hydrogen molecules are clearly established reactions. With more complex molecules the opportunities are far greater. Some can and do undergo fission under proper circumstances. Or they may undergo less violent transmutations to other elements. At the level of inorganic molecules, the possibilities are increased many fold. Organic molecules possess still greater latitude in the rearrangement of their component parts and their interactions with other elements and molecules.

Consider for a moment a polypeptide made up of the twenty alpha amino acids found in naturally occurring proteins. One can regard this as a very small protein molecule. In how many ways can one arrange these twenty amino acids, assuming there is one of each? Starting at the free amino end, it is clear that the molecule can begin with any one of the twenty amino acids. For each of these there can be any one of nineteen in the second position, any one of eighteen in the third, and so on, that is, $20 \times 19 \times 18 \times 17 \ldots \times 1$. That is called factorial 20, written "20!" How large is factorial 20? It is almost incomprehensibly large—more than 2 followed by 18 zeros, actually more than 2,432,902,-000,000,000,000. If we were to make all possible twenty amino-acid proteins, assuming all possible proportions of each amino acid and all possible orders, we see that any one of twenty can be in any one of the twenty positions. The total number is then $20 \times 20 \times 20 \ldots$ twenty times, or 20^{20}, which is *ten million times larger* than the 2 followed by 18 zeros!

The number of possible different protein molecules as large as the alpha chain of human hemoglobin, which has

150 amino acids, if all proportions and sequences of twenty amino acids are assumed, is 20^{150} or 10^{195}, that is, one followed by 195 zeros. The number of elementary particles in the entire known universe is estimated to be less than 10^{100}, a far smaller number.

Going one step further, in how many ways can we arrange five billion nucleotides of four kinds in a single chain, assuming again that all proportions and all orders are possible. The answer is a number followed by more than two billion zeros! Remember that five billion nucleotide pairs is the number in the nucleus of a single human cell. It should be abundantly clear, therefore, that at the level of complexity of man, the opportunities for evolution are essentially unlimited, even granting that almost all of those 10 raised to the two billionth power arrangements are nonsense in terms of specifying viable organisms.

What Is Life?

An interesting consequence of our remarkable recent advances in understanding simple living systems like viruses in terms of molecular structure and of the properties of nucleic acids and proteins is that the answer to the question of the distinction between nonliving and living systems has become increasingly arbitrary. Is a virus alive? It can reproduce and evolve, given a proper environment, which in this case is a complex cell of some clearly living organism. If a virus is living, how about an artificial DNA molecule? It too can reproduce and presumably evolve in a Kornberg test-tube system. If the answer is yes, what does one say about a mixture of DNA nucleotides as triphosphates in the Kornberg test-tube system? They can "evolve" into a DNA molecule capable of reproduction and further evolution. And so one could go on and on, finally ending up with the seemingly absurd question of whether hydrogen molecules are living. They too can evolve into complex systems that anyone would call living. As I say, the answer is arbitrary. Give me a precise definition of life and I shall have no trouble telling you whether a virus, DNA molecule, or a hydrogen atom is living. But I point out that your definition will be arbitrary, and necessarily so, given the present state of man's knowledge.

The Horowitz Hypothesis

The hypothesis outlined above assumes that a virus-like system made up of nucleic acid and protein was one of the early steps in the evolution of living systems as we commonly think of them. But how could such systems have reproduced in the absence of living cells to provide their building blocks? Our hypothesis assumes that the building blocks were spontaneously synthesized and available for use by the first "organism" as defined above. Eventually, however, living systems had to evolve the ability to direct the synthesis of such building blocks, for their origin by spontaneous reactions would be far too slow to permit evolution to proceed as it did. Also, as we know, today such spontaneously synthesized organic molecules have much less chance of surviving, first, because the earth's atmosphere has become oxidizing, and, second, because there are now many microorganisms that tear down such energy-rich molecules as nucleotides, amino acids, sugars, fats, etc.

The answer is that organisms must somehow have evolved the ability to direct the synthesis of their own building blocks from common inorganic molecules such as carbon dioxide, water, ammonia, nitrites and phosphates. But here again an apparent dilemma arises. A virus needs twenty kinds of amino acids to build its proteins and four kinds of nucleotides to copy its nucleic acids. To direct the synthesis of each of these from inorganic materials requires a source of energy plus the ability to direct catalytically a multistep chain of chemical reactions, each step presumably catalyzed by a specific protein. There is no advantage in carrying out only the first step in the chain, for, in general, the intermediate products in the reaction chain will serve no good purpose, certainly not as final building blocks. It is far too much to ask of mutation and natural selection that all the steps in such a reaction-chain evolve simultaneously.

Norman H. Horowitz was the first to point out a probable answer. He quite logically pointed out that a reaction chain could evolve one step at a time if the terminal step were first, the penultimate one second, and so on.

Assume a building block, BB_1, capable of being synthesized through the steps

$$A \longrightarrow B \longrightarrow C \longrightarrow D \longrightarrow BB_1$$

A first virus-like nucleoprotein would require that BB_1, as well as all other necessary building blocks, be present in the environment. This is reasonable, for if this first organism (let us call it O_1) itself arose, all its building blocks must have been present. As O_1 multiplied, using up preformed building blocks, including BB_1, it would occasionally become modified by mutation. Assume now that BB_1 became scarce so as to limit reproduction of O_1. If O_1 mutated so that its protein coat could catalyze the reaction $D \longrightarrow BB_1$, it could reproduce in the presence of either BB_1, or D. With BB_1 scarce the mutant form would replace its ancestral type, becoming O_2. As O_2 reproduced D too might become limiting. If a second mutation were to occur in O_2, giving O_3 which made a protein capable of catalyzing the reaction $C \longrightarrow D$, then O_2 and O_3 living symbiotically, perhaps as a two-gene system, could reproduce with

C or D or BB_1 present.   With D and BB_1 scarce, clearly O_2O_3 would replace O_2.

By successive mutations multigenic organisms presumably evolved capable of directing the synthesis of more and more of their building blocks until finally there appeared an autotrophic form capable of constructing all its building blocks from inorganic molecules.   Ultimately the source of energy for most such autotrophs became the sun.

The Ebb and Flow of the Evolutionary Tide

Evolutionary trends are ever changing.   There is no predetermined course.   Lines of descent are not always from simpler to more complex forms.   If simplification has advantages in a given environmental situation, then simpler forms will outbreed their competitors.

A classic example of an environment that favors simplification is that of many parasites.   Mutations involving loss of function are much more frequent than those that add or modify functions.   Parasites make use of building blocks of their hosts; hence there is often no selective advantage in their being able to synthesize them.   In fact, there is no doubt a selective advantage in not continuing to make them, for they are readily available from the host, and the nucleic-acid specifications that are no longer used are available for specifying new functions through mutation and natural selection.

The ultimate in known simplification of parasites is seen in the smaller and simpler viruses.   The tobacco mosaic virus, for example, is a simple rod-shaped organism with a core of RNA lying within a cyclindrical protein coat.   The RNA core consists of some 6,000 nucleotides and the protein units of the coat are relatively simple.   The $\phi X13$ bacterial virus has a core of DNA made up of some 5,500 nucleotides.   This is protected by a more or less spherical protein coat. The nucleic acids of these small viruses are believed to specify only a few proteins, one being the coat protein.

Whether present-day viruses are the end result of a long evolutionary process of simplification, are descended from early primitive forms of life without ever having a high degree of complexity, or are more or less immediately derived from the host cells which they now infect, we do not certainly know.

Differentiation

In almost all multicellular organisms cells differentiate and assume specialized functions. For example, mammalian red blood cells lose their nuclei and spend a good part of their resources in synthesizing the one protein, hemoglobin. Other cells make melanin pigments that give color to feathers, hair and skin. Others such as germ cells of animals and meristematic cells of growing regions of plants remain relatively unspecialized. How is it that cells whose nuclei carry identical genetic specifications use this information in so many diverse ways? While this is a question largely for future generations of biologists to answer, we are beginning to find a few clues.

Take melanin pigment formation, for example. In the Siamese cat this pigment is largely restricted to the extremities—the points. It is known that this is a relatively simple temperature effect. This variety of cat differs from fully pigmented cats, black ones for example, in having an altered form of the gene that specifies the enzyme tyrosinase, the enzyme that catalyzes oxidations of the amino acid tyrosine necessary to formation of melanin. This is a temperature-sensitive tyrosinase. At normal body temperature it is largely inactivated. But in regions a few degrees cooler, as the ears, nose, tail, and feet, the enzyme remains active and gives rise to pigmentation. As would be expected on this hypothesis, Siamese kittens are born white all over, for they have been at the mother's body temperature. About a week after birth pigment begins to appear in the points.

Another example of an environmental differential that triggers differential development of cells is found in the brown seaweed *Fucus*. The egg cell is spherically symmetrical. As it normally lies on the bottom of the shallow ocean waters in which it occurs, the rhizome (rootlike structure) appears on the bottom and the top part of the egg cuts off cells that will become the frondlike thallus of the seaweed. It is easy to show that the initial differential is environmental. A gradient of light, CO_2, hydrogen ions, oxygen, temperature, and certain chemicals artificially applied to the egg will specify the top-bottom axis of the young embryo that develops from the egg. With these the axis can be made to appear in any desired direction with respect to gravity.

Many enzymes are known to be "induced" to appear or increase greatly in amount by presence of substrate or related molecules. These are called inducible enzymes. They are presumed to be advantageous, for in the absence of the substrate for which they are specific they are not formed. The organism does not make the enzyme unless it is needed. This is, of course, a desirable kind of control mechanism from the organism's standpoint. In the absence of the inducer, enzyme formation is "repressed," presumably at the DNA or gene level. With the appearance of the end product, repression is often restored. Thus the genetic information may be "turned on" when needed and "turned off" when its task is completed.

In the colon bacillus, François Jacob and co-workers at the Pasteur Institute in Paris have described such systems in considerable detail. It is clear that in addition to structural genes that specify enzymes there are "control" genes concerned with turning structural genes on and off. Some control genes appear to "send" messages and others "receive" them preparatory to transmitting instructions somehow to the structural genes under their jurisdiction.

Structural differentiation of cytoplasmic elements occurs in many, probably all, cells. Some such structures are "copied" from preexisting structures. This is true of cytoplasmic structures in the protozoan *Paramecium,* for example. In these remarkable cells in which a high degree of specialization of organelles occurs within a single cell, it appears that nuclear and cytoplasmic information evolves in parallel and in one sense more or less independently.

External Information

During the development of any organism, the environment continuously supplies information of many kinds. The example of the Siamese cat and the *Fucus* egg illustrate this. Raw material in the form of food, vitamins, temperature, oxygen, carbon dioxide, and a host of others are a part of the total information.

The Nervous System

Higher animals are distinguished from their simpler relatives and from plants in having specialized nervous systems. We among all species on earth have gone farthest in this direction. Our storage, retrieval, and reasoning capacities exceed by far those of any other species. Unfortunately, we do not know much about how our remarkable nervous systems work in these respects. This, again, is a problem for future generations of biologists. But we do know that information is fed into our brains from the time of birth and before. And we know that this has profound effects on our development. We have no way of measuring the total information contained in a normal adult human brain. We know it is a great deal, but we do not know whether it is less or more than that carried in the DNA of a single cell.

Our highly developed nervous systems make possible memory, reason, and communication. These are the bases of our cultural inheritance which includes language, art, religion, music, literature, technology, and science. We acquire it during our individual lives and we pass it on to future generations in a cumulative fashion.

Science, itself a part of our cultural inheritance, enables us to understand our origins, our evolution, our development, our biological inheritance, and our cultural inheritance. It has given us the knowledge by which we can direct the evolution of the plants and animals whose futures are of interest and importance to us.

Our knowledge is such that we could, if we chose to do so, direct our own evolutionary futures. Unfortunately, our wisdom is all too poorly developed to trust ourselves to do this intelligently. Until we can do better—and that will probably not be for a long, long time—we had best play safe and maintain a high degree of genetic diversity among men, that is, within the normal range, for in that way we can assure for future generations maximum evolutionary flexibility.

Genetic Disease in Man

Many unfavorable mutations in man are expressed as genetic diseases. Albinism, galactosemia, muscular dystrophy, hemophilia, cystic fibrosis, Huntington's chorea.

phenylketonuria, alcaptonuria, and many others are examples. Several hundred are now known, some well, other less well. As nutritional and infectious diseases are increasingly prevented or controlled, genetic diseases become relatively more important. They are kept from building up in frequency with successive generations, like those errors in the case of the mechanical typist, by natural selection.

Through knowledge of the genetic and biochemical nature of genetic diseases, medical science has devised ways of circumventing some of them. For example, galactosemia may be circumvented through the use of a galactose-free diet in early life. This is not a "cure," for the faulty DNA specifications are not corrected.

Circumvention of genetic disease confronts medicine and society with a dilemma, for if persons with such diseases are treated in such a way that they become reproductively normal and do in fact reproduce normally, the incidence of the circumvented diseases will build up in future generations. Fortunately, the buildup will be slow. It may require thousands of years to reach an incidence of one affected person per thousand for a particular disease. If the number of genetic diseases so circumvented becomes large, the problem will become correspondingly more serious and urgent.

One simple way to prevent this buildup caused by removing or reducing the control of natural selection is to persuade affected individuals to adopt children instead of producing their own.

Evolution and Materialism

The view of evolution I have presented may seem mechanical, materialistic, and Godless beyond all possible acceptance. This is not a new reaction. The publication of the *Origin of Species* immediately raised this objection in the minds of many. Thomas Henry Huxley in a famous lecture in Edinburgh gave the answer some seventy years ago and it is still a good answer. He said that the mere use of methodology and terminology of materialism does not make a person a materialist any more than wearing material clothes and eating material food does. Nothing that I have said about evolution changes in any way the nature of the basic question of ultimate creation or the existence of a Creator. In many ways it is just as remarkable, just as awesome, just as inspiring, and just as satisfying to believe in the creation of a universe of hydrogen endowed with the potentiality of evolving into a human being as it is to believe in a universe in which man was created as man. And there is a great deal more evidence for the former.

REFERENCES

ANFINSEN, C. B. 1959. *The Molecular Basis of Evolution.* (New York, John Wiley & Sons, Inc.).

Britannica Book of the Year 1963, Article on Biochemistry, pp. 207–208. 1963.

CRICK, F. H. C. 1963. On the genetic code. *Science* 139: 461–464.

HOROWITZ, N. H., and S. L. MILLER. 1962. Current Theories on the Origin of Life. *Fortschritte der Chemie organisher Naturstoffe* 20: 423–459.

JOHNSON, W. H., and W. C. STEERE, Editors. 1962. *Essays in Modern Biology: This is Life* (New York, Holt, Rinehart and Winston).

NIRENBERG, M. W. March 1963. The genetic code II. *Scientific American* 208: 80–94.

SAGER, R., and F. J. RYAN. 1961. *Cell Heredity* (New York, John Wiley & Sons, Inc.).

STERN, C. 1960. *Principles of Human Genetics* (ed. 2, San Francisco, W. H. Freeman & Co.).